Paws off My
CANNON

BRAVE
BOOKS

DOM-A-TRON

THE OLD ISLANDS

Burrycanter

Doomsdome

UTOPIA

Freedom Island

WIGGAMORE WOOD

SUMA SAVANNA

Rushington

Hive Have

Furenzy park

Toke-A-Toke

Wonder Well

Capitol

Mushroom Village

Deserted Desert

Mt. Avalerif

RAKA RAIN FOREST

Sky Tree

Snapfast Meadow

CAR-A-LAGO COAST

Starlotte City

Gray Landing

Home of the Brave

Shivermore

Nogard Cavern

MONOCK MOUNTAINS

Meltonville

CABAL ISLAND

Temple of The Serpent

Welcome to **Freedom Island**, Home of the Brave, where good battles evil and truth prevails. Years ago, the legends of Freedom Island fought to create a free nation. Save the animals of Mushroom Village by completing the BRAVE Challenge at the end of this book.

Watch this video for an introduction to the story and BRAVE Universe!

Saga One: The Origins
Book 6

Paws off My Cannon

Saga One: The Origins—Book 6

Paws off My Cannon

Book Illustrations © 2021 by André Ceolin
Map Illustration © 2021 by Ali Elzeiny

Published by BRAVE BOOKS
www.BRAVEbooks.us

ISBN: 978-1-955550-05-5 (paperback)

First edition published in the USA in 2021 by BRAVE BOOKS

Printed in Canada

Paws off My
CANNON

Dana Loesch and **BRAVE BOOKS**

Art by **André Ceolin**

Bongo loved food.

In particular, Bongo loved cupcakes, which is why he lived in Mushroom Village.

Every night, Bongo and the other villagers sat around the Rockin' Rollin' River eating delicious mushroom shaped cupcakes, with loads of red and blue and green icing.

But one night, the picnic went terribly wrong.

A hungry hyena sprang onto the riverbank waving a coconut cannon. Bongo's best friend Bonnie squealed, "The hyenas are here for our cupcake dinners!"

The hyena, quick-as-a-flash, grabbed her picnic basket full of sweets.

Bongo chased the hyena in circles and squares, but ...

Cha-BAM!

Bongo and Bonnie landed flat on their bums, with bulbous bumps growing on their heads. Before they could count to five, the hyena was half way home to the Deserted Desert.

Hyenas were the only bad thing about living in Mushroom Village. They were lazy and didn't like cooking, so they roamed around looking for a sweet meal to steal.

Right away, the leader of the town called a meeting. "Poor Bongo and Bonnie! We must find a way to stop all this violence."

Bonnie spoke up. "We should make a rule and write it on a big sign: no one can bring coconut cannons into Mushroom Village. Then we'll be safe!"

"Right on!" said half the village.

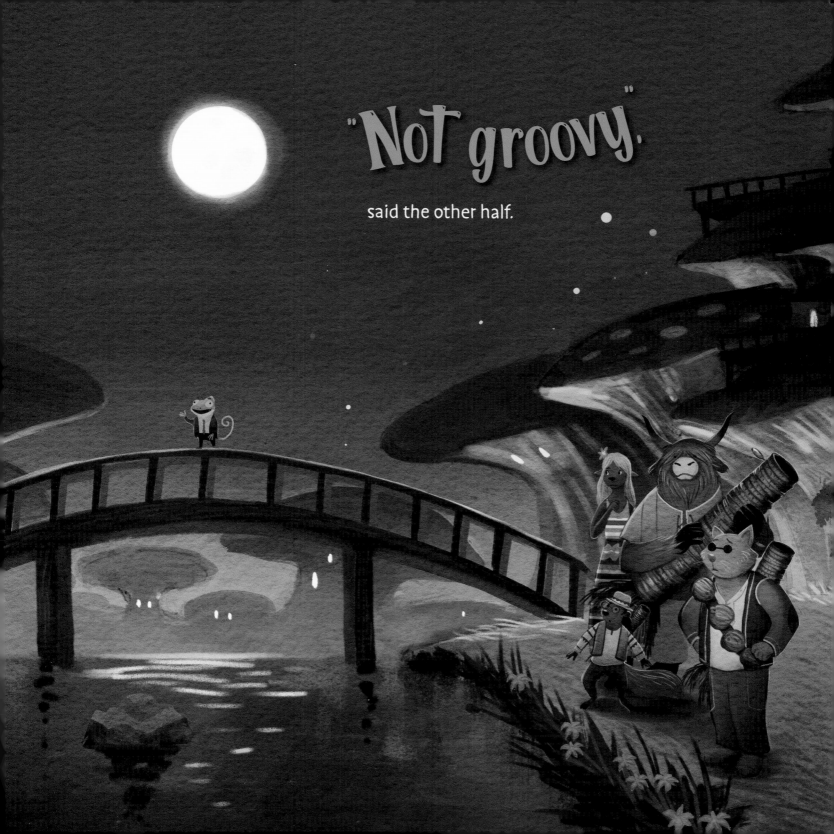

"Not groovy."

said the other half.

"Coconut cannons are how we protect ourselves!" Bongo rubbed his head. "We should keep our cannons close in case the hyenas come back."

"Silly Bongo!" Bonnie said, "If you disagree with us, we'll have to split Mushroom Village in half, and it'll be all your fault. Then we'll know who's really safe."

After arguing back and forth, forth and back, the village split down the middle.

On the west side, the villagers put all the cannons away. Bonnie smiled as she threw hers into the river, but Bongo knew it was a mistake.

Sighing a deep sigh, Bongo packed
up all his cannons and pushed them
across the river to the east.

Then Bonnie's side tore down
the bridge and made signs:

NO CANNONS HERE

STILL NO CANNONS

NO COCONUT CANNONS ALLOWED

The next morning, Bonnie and the animals on the west ate their cupcake breakfast without fear.

"The signs will protect us," Bonnie said.

On the east bank, Bongo strapped extra coconuts to his chest, just in case—and it was a good thing, too. Just as he was about to bite into his green and purple breakfast cupcake, a watchdog howled: "Hyenas on the horizon!"

Bonnie just glanced at the hyenas and shrugged.

"They can't bring their cannons to our side," she said.

Bongo jumped up and gripped his cannon.

"They've come for breakfast."

Cha-BOOM

went the hyenas' coconuts.

Cha-BASH

went Bongo's cannon.

In five seconds flat, Bongo and his buddies had given all the hyenas their own bulbous bumps, and quick-as-a-flash, they scrambled away.

But they didn't run back to the Deserted Desert. The hyenas leapt across the river to the west side of the village, and Bonnie gasped. "They broke the rule! The sign *specifically* says they can't bring their cannons!"

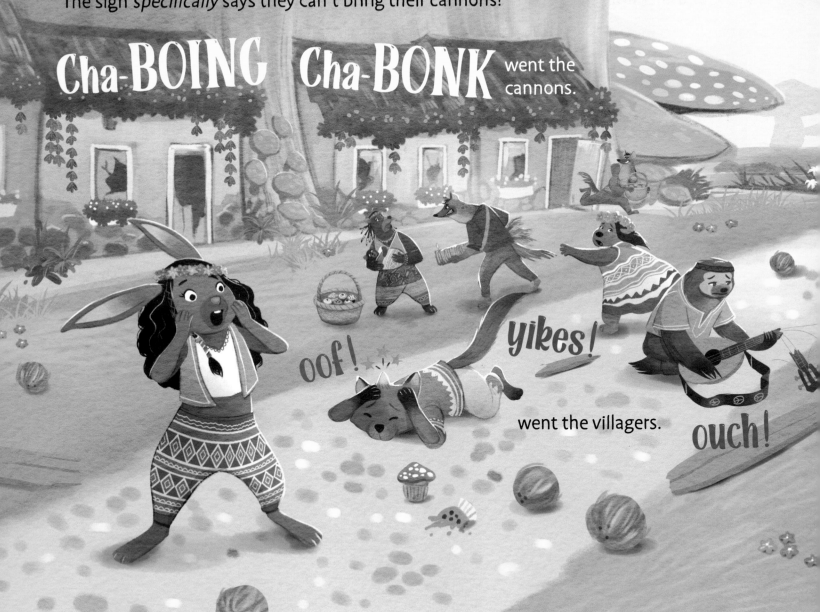

Before long, the hyenas had taken all of the cupcake breakfasts on the whole west side of Mushroom Village, and not a single animal was left without a coconut-shaped bump.

After the hyenas fled, Bongo stood, biting his nails. What if the hyenas hurt Bonnie? But the sign was still standing, and the rule was in place: no coconut cannons on the west side of the village.

Slowly, Bongo set down his cannon.

Swiftly, he swam across the river.

Silently, he crept through the crumbling town.

Phew! There was Bonnie, bruised but not battered. Bongo scooped her up and helped her stand.

"The hyenas do not obey our laws," Bonnie announced. "If we want to protect ourselves, we must be ready to fight back."

The animals nodded. They tore down the sign and bound up their bumps.

When the hyenas returned for lunch, they were dazed and confused. Every animal in Mushroom Village was armed with a weapon, and Bongo stood at their head.

"Lunch is served," Bongo growled.

After a **Cha-BASH** and a few **Cha-BOPs**, the hyenas bounded away, howling and whining, tummies grumbling grumpily.

And so, that night the picnic continued.

Bongo and the other villagers sat around the Rockin' Rollin' River eating delicious mushroom shaped cupcakes, with loads of purple and yellow and orange icing.

They ate in peace because they knew Bongo would protect them with his coconut cannons.

Bongo loved food, but most of all, Bongo loved his village.

Dear Bongo,

The courageous use their strength, not to hide, but to defend the defenseless.

Your eagerness to protect your village, without sacrificing honor or integrity, shows a strength of your character far beyond your years. Freedom Island needs heroes like you.

If you are willing to defend our dear island, answer the call. Journey to Wizards Way by the first day of fall.

Hurry. Our nation cannot hold back these dark forces much longer.

Anticipating your speedy arrival—
The Legends of Freedom Island

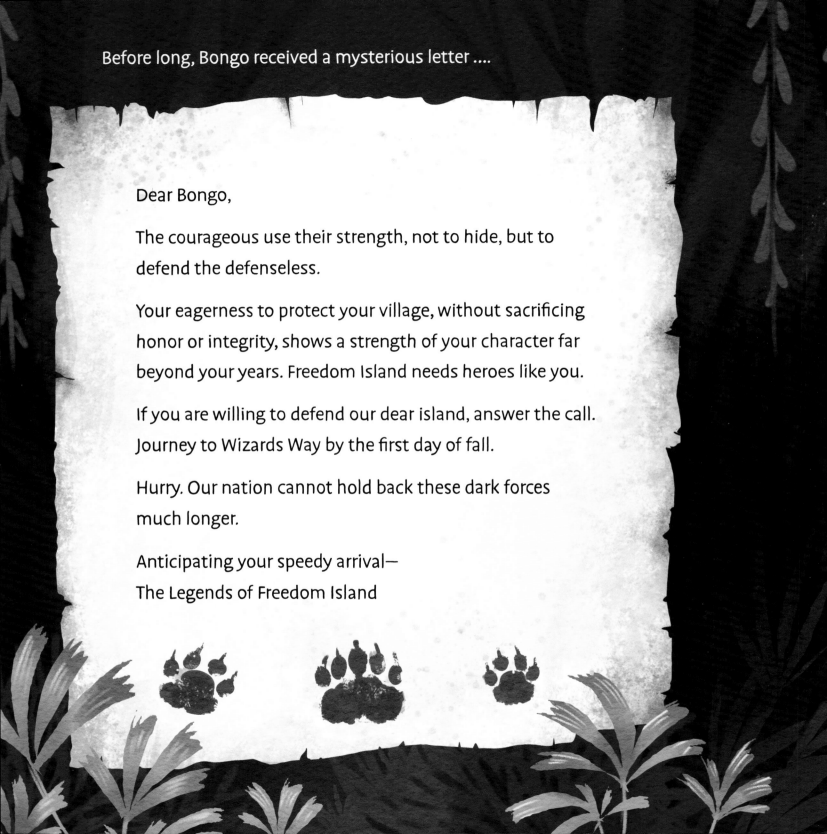

TO YOUR FAMILY

INTRODUCTION

BRAVE Books has created the BRAVE Challenge to drive home key lessons and values illustrated in the story. Each activity takes between 10 and 20 minutes. Family-focused and collaborative, the BRAVE Challenge is a quick and fun option for family game night.

BRAVE CHALLENGE KEY

 Read aloud to the children

 One child modification

 For parents only

 Roll the die for the Hyenas

THE BRAVE CHALLENGE

 ### OBJECTIVE

Welcome to Team BRAVE! Your mission for this BRAVE Challenge is to defend Mushroom Village from the terrible hyenas. To get started, grab a sheet of paper and a pencil, and draw a scoreboard titled Team BRAVE vs. Team Hyenas, like the one shown.

Team BRAVE	Team Hyenas

While the children create the scoreboard, decide on a reward for victory. Here are a few ideas:

- *Baking cupcakes or cookies*
- *Going swimming*
- *Movie night*
- *Playing the children's favorite game*
- *Buying candy bars*
- *Riding bikes*
- *Whatever gets your kiddos excited!*

HOW TO PLAY

In this BRAVE Challenge, Team BRAVE (the children) will compete against Team Hyenas to earn points. As each team earns points, keep track on the scoreboard you just created. At the end of all three activities, the team with the most points wins.

WINNING

At the end, if Team BRAVE has earned more points than the hyenas, then they have successfully defended Mushroom Village. The prize for winning will be _____. Let's begin!

INTRODUCING...

DANA LOESCH

Dana Loesch is a conservative political commentator and popular influencer who has spent her career bringing awareness to issues such as Second Amendment rights. She helped BRAVE Books write this story and the BRAVE Challenge. She will be popping in to give you ideas on how you can explain these concepts to your child.

DANA SUGGESTS

"Hi, parents! I hope you have a great time playing the games and that they create fruitful conversations!"

THE SECOND AMENDMENT

The Second Amendment to the US Constitution was written in 1791 to ensure that all Americans have the right to bear arms in order to protect themselves. The Second Amendment reads: "A well regulated Militia, being necessary to the security of a free State, the right of the people to keep and bear Arms, shall not be infringed."

LESSON

It's important to be able to protect yourself.

MATERIALS NEEDED

A six-sided die and a blanket.

Video Tutorial

 ## OBJECTIVE

Team BRAVE, Mushroom Village is split! You must help the villagers decide what they can use for protection from all sorts of dangers. Identify if something will protect you or not by jumping to either Bongo's side or Bonnie's side of the river (blanket).

 ## INSTRUCTIONS

 Before starting, roll the die to see how many points the Hyenas earned. **Record this number on the scoreboard.**

1. Place a blanket on the floor to imitate a river, and designate one side as Bongo's and one side as Bonnie's.
2. Team BRAVE lines up on the blanket.
3. A parent reads from the list of words below, one at a time.
4. Team BRAVE will then decide if that thing would help protect them or not.
   a. If the word describes something that is used for protection, Team BRAVE should first, jump to Bongo's side of the blanket, and second, pretend to use the object.
   b. If the object would not help protect them, Team BRAVE should jump to Bonnie's side of the blanket and again pretend to use the object.

5. Team BRAVE starts out with 6 points; for each mistake, they lose 1 point.
6. ***Record Team BRAVE's final score on the scoreboard.***

Game on!

Parents say:

- **Baseball bat**. *Yes, Bongo's side*
- **Life jacket.** *Yes, Bongo's side*
- **Banana.** *No, Bonnie's side*
- **Bike helmet.** *Yes, Bongo's side*
- **Smelly sock.** *No, Bonnie's side*
- **Seat belt.** *Yes, Bongo's side*
- **Coconut cannon**. *Yes, Bongo's side*
- **Juice box**. *No, Bonnie's side*

─── **BRAVE TIP** ───

Parents can think of other objects to keep the game going!

TALK ABOUT IT

1. Why is it important to have things that will protect you?
2. In the story, how did Bongo protect Mushroom Village?
3. Who should use a firearm? Why would it be helpful for adults to have a firearm?
4. Should you play with a firearm?

DANA SUGGESTS

"Part of the responsibility of owning a firearm is proper discipline in gun safety. Firearms are not toys; they are powerful tools and should be respected as such. When used wisely, however, they can be a powerful means of protection."

GAME #2 - HYENA IN THE MIDDLE

LESSON

Be a good steward of what you have been given.

MATERIALS NEEDED

A ball and a timer.

Video Tutorial

 ## OBJECTIVE

You are still protecting Mushroom Village and your food from the hyenas. You must keep your cupcake (ball) away from a hungry hyena by passing it between members of Team BRAVE.

 ## INSTRUCTIONS

1. Team BRAVE forms a circle.
2. A parent stands in the middle of the circle to act as the hyena. The hyena will try to tag whoever holds the ball.
3. Choose one member of Team BRAVE to start with the ball.
4. Set a timer for two minutes.
5. The first BRAVE member will toss the ball to another player. Whoever is holding the ball must stand in place until he or she has tossed it to someone else.
6. Team Brave starts with 10 points and loses a point for each time the hyena successfully tags them.
7. The hyena starts with 0 points and earns one point for each successful tag.
8. **Record the final score on the scoreboard.**

Ready? Begin!

ONE CHILD MODIFICATION

Pretend you and your parent are on the roofs of Mushroom Village. Toss a cupcake (a ball) back and forth to each other. After each successful toss, both players take one step back and toss again.

Your goal is to throw the food back and forth 10 times without dropping it down to the hyenas below. You gain one point for every successful catch.

Game on!

TALK ABOUT IT

1. During the game, was it hard to protect the cupcake from the hyenas?
2. Why is protecting your property important?

DANA SUGGESTS

"Someone had to work hard to buy or make the things that we own. It is our responsibility to take good care of everything that we own and not be wasteful."

"Know well the condition of your flocks,
and give attention to your herds."
Proverbs 27:23 (ESV)

3. How do the ideas of protection and responsibility go together?

DANA SUGGESTS

"Protection and responsibility go hand-in-hand. As a leader, if you are put in a position of responsibility, one of the main aspects of that responsibility is to protect and care for the people you lead."

LESSON

Things do not go well when you lose the ability to protect yourself.

MATERIALS NEEDED

Six cupcakes (or objects to act as cupcakes) and six plush balls.

Video Tutorial

─── **BRAVE TIP** ───

 Feel free to substitute cupcakes for any yummy snack. Balls can be any soft item, including sock balls or wadded up paper balls.

📣 OBJECTIVE

The hyenas are hungry and attacking! Team BRAVE, you must protect yourself and your cupcakes from the hyenas (parents).

📣 INSTRUCTIONS

Setup for Round One: All BRAVE members start with one arm behind their backs. Nearby, they have a stash of six cupcakes and one ball.

Setup for Round Two: Team BRAVE can use both arms, and they have six cupcakes as well as six balls.

─── **BRAVE TIP** ───

 If throwing balls inside is a concern, use wadded up paper instead.

Gameplay:

1. The hyenas (parents) start on the other side of the room with full use of their arms and no balls.

2. When the game begins, parents will run towards Team BRAVE to take their cupcakes. Each hyena can take only one cupcake at a time, and must set it down on the hyenas side of the room before coming for another one.

3. To protect the food, Team BRAVE can throw their one ball (round one) or their six balls (round two) at the parents.

4. The round ends when Team BRAVE successfully hits the hyenas a total of six times OR when all the cupcakes have been taken.

5. Until Team BRAVE lands the sixth hit, the hyenas will keep running, so be quick!

6. At the end of each round, count the cupcakes on each side. The hyenas get one point for each cupcake stolen and Team BRAVE gets one point for each remaining cupcake.

7. ***Record the final score after each round on the scoreboard.***

Game on!

 BRAVE TIP

 After the game is over, if Team BRAVE is able to gather all six balls and cupcakes and put them away within thirty seconds, they can receive an additional point

 # TALK ABOUT IT

1. Why was round two of the game much easier? Did more balls make it easier to protect the cupcakes?

2. In the story, did the laws on Bonnie's side protect those animals? Why not?

DANA SUGGESTS

"There will always be bad people who break the law and do bad things. This is why we cannot rely on laws alone to protect ourselves."

3. Bongo left his coconut cannon on his side when he went to find Bonnie. Why do you think he did that?

DANA SUGGESTS

"Although Bongo knew it was a risk, he respected his government and the law of the land. Bongo obeyed the law when it put him in danger—even as he worked to change that law for the good of the community."

TALLY ALL THE POINTS TO SEE WHO WON!

BRAVE SUMMARY

The world we live in is not perfect, so there will always be hyenas who try to hurt others. Some people, like Bonnie, believe that laws against guns and signs saying "No Weapons Allowed" will make them safe. Sadly, the people who want to hurt others often don't care about laws, and they take advantage of those who do obey those rules. The Second Amendment to the Constitution protects your right to own a gun so that you can defend your family, yourself, and others from those who want to hurt you. Guns are powerful, so we must be very careful, but in the long run, guns provide a protection that is well worth the risk.

Submit comments to: Feedback@BRAVE.us